SOLD FOR A SONG

SOLD FOR A SONG

A STUDY OF AN ARABIAN MONGOOSE

by

CLARE KIPPS
(Author of *Sold For a Farthing*)

Illustrated by

L. R. BRIGHTWELL

FREDERICK MULLER LTD
LONDON

PUBLISHED BY FREDERICK MULLER LTD
AND PRINTED IN GREAT BRITAIN BY
BILLING AND SONS LTD., GUILDFORD AND LONDON

COPYRIGHT, 1956, CLARE KIPPS
SECOND IMPRESSION, JULY 1956

CONTENTS

Dedicated to

Dr Patricia Ruth Elliott, M.B., B.SC.
Member of the Order of the British Empire and
Founder of St. Andrew's Orthopædic Hospital for
Children, Singapore

What is sin but that which offends Love: what is self-sacrifice but joy in the service of Love: what is repentance but spontaneous sorrow for having grieved Love: what is Communion but joy and replenishment in the Presence of Love: and what then is worship but the inevitable, effortless recognition of Love Ineffable?

PROLOGUE

There are moments, especially as we advance in years, when we look back and take stock of the friends who made life richer or poorer according to the quality of their friendship.

Such is this moment to me, and as I turn to gaze into the still-glowing mid-distance of more than thirty years ago, I see, standing out quite clearly from among the rest, a tiny figure that has climbed on to the shoulder of a beloved grey-haired woman and is looking in my direction.

He stands there, this little creature, erect, poised perfectly on his very short hind legs, his lovely fur coat brown and glistening, his little paws pressed close against his chest. Yes—and there is his little nose, tilted high into the air, and his sharp bright eyes looking down it with that absurdly quizzical, supercilious air that was so characteristic of him.

I lift my hand to wave to him: but now, suddenly, the vision fades, and something catches at my throat when I remember that, among the many friends who brought me happiness (often far beyond my deserving) he is the only one that I deliberately, though regretfully, betrayed.

And so perhaps it is to calm a still faintly-accusing conscience, and to make up to him in some small measure for that betrayal, that I venture now to make him the hero of this little book.

He was, I understood, an Arabian Mongoose, and the somewhat incongruous name that I bestowed upon him (the relevance of which will be discovered later) was Carter Paterson. He lived with me very happily for three years, but I know nothing of his earlier or later life; nor did I ever find anyone who could inform me of his age, though I feel sure that he was quite young. All that I have to record of him was contained in that short space of time during which he taught me much, and became a personality so distinct, so exclusive and so original, that no-one who ever knew him has yet been found to have forgotten him.

I always feel that a man or woman who has never known the love and trust of bird or beast has missed a very precious thing. I believe we have all a great responsibility to those that are in our care; but, make no mistake about it, a human Life is of greater importance than an animal's, and those who think otherwise are surely wrong. And so eventually, having provided for the safety and well-being of my little friend to the best of my ability, I accepted a tour abroad in the professional capacity for which I had been trained, and which, alas, compelled my separation from him. He was taken away one night, in the warmly-padded box in which he slept, to a private Zoo where he was loved and valued, and where friends visited him and assured me that he had settled down, had mated and appeared to be content. I never saw the going of him. I wanted to remember him as he was in our last hours together. Neither did I ever visit him; but that was for his own sake, and because I feared I could not look into his eyes. I took no money for him, for friendship such as he had bestowed upon me was surely beyond price.

On my return from the Far East I brought back with me an Indian Ichneumon, a much larger and more virile beast, with coarse grey fur and immense muscular strength, who also lived with me for three years.

The two mongooses, although they never met, had of course many characteristics in common, notably the insatiable, exuberant curiosity, and the wonderful rapidity and accuracy of movement. But as a personality the Indian lagged so *far* behind his little predecessor that I have introduced him briefly into this Prologue solely by way of contrast, and to prove how truly justified is the modern belief that animals are individuals, and may differ from other members of their own species as widely as one human being does from another.

An affectionate pet, he would leap into my arms with a boisterous welcome even after a short separation; but he was friendly with everyone and completely fearless. Specially beloved by schoolboys, to whom he was indeed an "embodied joy," he would romp with them for hours after he had unfastened their ties, bootlaces, buttons and even braces, turned their pockets inside out and confiscated everything small and detachable from their persons.

Being very destructive, he was controlled, as is not uncommon with the Indian Mongoose in captivity, by a collar and lead to save my home from demolition; for he had made his first appearance in it memorable by tearing out all the electric flexes that he found on his tour of inspection, quite undeterred by a severe shock from which he recovered after an astonishing display of acrobatics and bad language. No doubt he thought them very vicious, and in some way related to the snakes whom his family had sworn to destroy from time immemorial.

In the end I think he must have heard the call of the jungle, for he became so restless and lovesick that I sold him to a man who had a collection of small mammals, and I understood that he too took a wife and lived in great connubial contentment.

For my part, attractive though he undoubtedly was, I was glad to see him go. In an empty heart there is always room for memories, and there were many that I treasured of my little friend from Arabia—the tiny poet-soul with his gentle ways, his almost Lewis-Carroll-like sense of fun, his touch of mysticism and his gift for intimate and hallowed friendship—whom I hasten now to introduce.

CHAPTER ONE

THE ENCOUNTER

Far are the shades of Arabia
Where the Princes ride at noon
In the verdurous vales and thickets
Under the ghost of the Moon.
Walter de la Mare.

I first met him in Camden Town, and in peculiarly distressing circumstances, in the year nineteen hundred and twenty-three.

Squandering an hour, stolen from my studies, in aimless wandering one dull November afternoon, my attention was arrested by the sound of loud coarse laughter; and, turning to ascertain the cause of it, I saw a group of rough lads obviously teasing, prodding and tormenting some unhappy creature in the open front of a junk-shop which has long since disappeared.

Pushing my way hurriedly through these young savages, I saw a long low cage, and in it a little long, low, furry animal with a neat little head, very short legs and a thick tail that tapered to a point and was about the same length as its body. In all, from nose-tip to tail-end, I should have said it measured about eighteen inches. It belonged, I imagined, to the same family as the Civets, and was a little like a ferret in a dark fur coat, but with a straighter back and without its cruel and evil look.

The creature was dirty, blear-eyed and desperately weary; and one at least of its little feet was bleeding as was evident from the red tracks in the sand: for, except when it stopped to cringe and spit at its persecutors, it went round and round the floor of its prison, driven continually and remorselessly on like a soul in torment.

I find its movements a little difficult to describe. It half slunk and half hurried, furtively, despairingly and yet restlessly; and

5

the smooth monotony of its pace suggested a nervous pent-up energy that was capable I felt sure of very great speed, but which had almost reached the point of exhaustion.

Moved by the sight of so much misery, I entered the shop and enquired if the animal were for sale, and if so what would be the price of him.

"I'll let yer 'ave 'im for thirty bob," said the shopman: "and I'll throw in the cage for another ten because if I tried to get 'old of the little brute I'd never set eyes on 'im again. It's dirt cheap, mind you," he went on, "but 'e's a crazy beast and I can't do nothing with 'im."

He described the creature as an Arabian Mongoose, and told me that an Army man had brought him from Arabia, hoping he would make an amusing pet; but he had found him so intractable and incapable of affection that he had been thankful to "get shot of him for a song."

"There is nothing that suggests a song about him now," I murmured: but the man looked at me stupidly and made no reply. In the end, after being assured—almost on oath—that the Army man had left no address, and no information by means of which I could trace him and learn more of the Mongoose's history and background, I produced—though with some difficulty, for students are seldom rich—the sum of two pounds and counted the money into the salesman's filthy hand. Then I carried the cage with its wretched occupant in my aching arms to A—— Street where, being at that time a student at the Royal Academy of Music, I rented two rooms in the house of a woman Doctor who was much beloved in the neighbourhood.

Dropping my burden quietly and thankfully on to my bed-settee—for I could carry it no further—I tried, with gentle voice and gesture, and every available offering of food that I hoped might appeal to him, to comfort and reassure the little exile. But it was all in vain. When I spoke to him he cowered and spat at me; and when I moved away the awful circumambulation began again. In despair I covered his cage with a piece of dark warm felt, out of respect for his sorrows, and went in search of the Doctor. She had been born in India, and had spent most of

6

her life there; and she might know the way to a frightened little Mongoose's heart.

"Oh!" she said very quietly as she looked down at him, "he'll be all right if you give him something to *hide* in. Mongooses are all like that. They like to *see without being seen*. Then, in their own time, they will choose a human being that they like the look of and, given a little encouragement and a saucer of bread and milk, will make his home their headquarters. They are very friendly to man out East and will keep a bungalow free of snakes: but *they* like to make the first move and to be allowed to feel that they are favouring him with their distinguished patronage. For after all, you know, they *are* the aristocrats of their own family and are very highly respected in the jungle.

"I think I know what you can do," she continued after a moment's cogitation. "Take a wide, loosely-made sleeve out of that shabby old knitted dress of yours. Tie the shoulder-end firmly to the wires of the cage and push the rest of it through the bars on to its floor with the cuff gaping invitingly open. Then stand quite still and watch what happens."

This was done: and, before there had been time to "watch" anything, a very great deal had happened. The Mongoose was in the sleeve and, because in the jungle a man always sleeps with his face towards the front door, he had turned round in it and had settled down with his nose close to the cuff-end.

Then there was silence and the little wild thing was at rest. Peace had come to him at last after the long day's anguish, while a kindly covering darkness wrapped him round. And it had come softly and suddenly, like a tropical nightfall to the agony of the desert.

With a full heart I replaced the cover on the cage: and for hours afterwards, while I moved quietly about my little flat, prepared and ate my simple supper and then sat reading over my studio fire, the only sound that could be heard was the gentle ticking of my little clock. I think my lodger must have slept from sheer exhaustion, for when I peeped cautiously under his dark blanket, the grey woollen sleeve looked for all the world like a Christmas stocking, and the bulge in it like a soft mysterious parcel left by

St. Nicholas for an unknown child. Indeed it was so utterly without sound or stir that I was suddenly afraid and wondered if the little fellow could have died in his sleep: but a muffled curse when I called a soft goodnight to him as I slid wearily into bed assured me that he was alive.

This was his home-coming; but for the next ten days I never caught so much as a glimpse of a disappearing tail. Fresh water, and food of various kinds, such as bread-and-milk, yolk of hard-boiled egg, fruit, and dainty little pieces of lightly-cooked meat, were placed regularly in his cage and as regularly disappeared.

I never saw them go, but I knew that he was eating well; and, as there were no red stains in the fresh sand on his prison-floor, I gathered that his wounds had healed. There was plenty of evidence also that he was making free use of his cage when he was alone in the room, so, on the whole, everything appeared to be going well. He must surely be gaining strength, I thought, and one day no doubt he would find courage also.

So long as I refrained from addressing him or taking liberties of any kind, he made no attempt at conversation. He just "lay low" like Brer Rabbit and said nothing. But I very soon became conscious of the fact that I myself was being kept continually under close observation and began to realize that he was studying *me* far more intensively than I (in my crude amateur way, I have no doubt he thought) was studying him. This was quite in keeping with what the Doctor had told me of the mentality of the Mongoose, and I fancied he was already far ahead of me in this interesting interchange of elementary psychological and physiological research. However, I felt that I could at least congratulate myself when I discovered that he *spat* at people when he was afraid of them or considered them beneath contempt, and *growled* at them when he felt they should be afraid of him or should treat him with more respect. (And here I think I should explain that by "spat" I mean that he made a violent spitting sound without any ejection of fluid.) He was obviously a man of few words and, except for these two forcible and eloquent expressions, he was—and remained as long as I was privileged to know him—as taciturn as an Okapi.

The Doctor lived in a tall, narrow, cream-washed terrace-house of the Regency period, separated by iron railings from the pavement of a busy street, and with steps leading up to a heavy red front door. It consisted of a basement, in which lived the deaf but worthy housekeeper, and four floors, each containing two rooms. I occupied the second floor, and enjoyed the amenities of a small kitchen, and a studio-bedroom. The latter was a long room, its ceiling just low enough to give a sense of protection and intimacy. It had two good windows opening on to the street; and at the far end from the door was an old-fashioned grate with hobs, like those in the original illustrations of Dickens, in which I kept a glowing fire of coal in the winter months.

A boudoir grand piano, a bed-settee, an old oak chest, a small round table, a tall oak cupboard and some cosy chairs supplied my daily needs; while for the delight of my eyes and the sustenance of my soul I had added some beloved books, a Kerman rug, curtains and cushions of soft harmonious hues, a bowl of flowers and a few pictures and statuettes.

The Mongoose's cage, I blush to say, stood permanently on the grand piano (which was protected by a rug of exquisite colouring), for the simple reason that no other place could be found for it.

At first, for fear of disturbing the little creature and perhaps retarding his convalescence, I moved about the house as cautiously as if I were a fugitive from justice and in continual fear of arrest. I ate my meals in the kitchen; and my studio was often silent and deserted except at night. This of course was patently absurd, and for two reasons. First; because, however much one loves an animal, one *must* keep a sense of proportion; and secondly, because there was no need for such self-effacement. The little animal in question was not dying, and the sooner he became accustomed to the sights and sounds of his new home the better for his peace of mind. Moreover, to waste any appreciable part of a long-coveted and dearly-bought opportunity of studying a great art on account of a Mongoose with a nervous breakdown savoured of insanity!

At the end of a week, therefore, I resumed my steady patient hours of daily practice, and as students of animal behaviour are often interested in the reactions of wild animals to music, a brief description of the effect (or lack of effect) of this practice on the Mongoose may not be out of place here. I started off, as a delicate gesture of sympathy to the little exile, with a tender rendering of "Home, Sweet Home," but it was completely wasted on him. There was not the slighest indication that he had even noticed it; so I forgot him and went on to discuss weightier matters at the keyboard. It struck me later when I thought it over that there was something very peculiar about his complete indifference to music. He might have been dead or at least stone-deaf for all the effect it had on him, and I knew that he was neither. A sudden crashing Forzando, for instance, left him completely unmoved: and the opening of Tchaikovski's great B flat minor concerto made no more impression on him than my faint but persistent efforts to discover and reproduce Pachmann's "Seventeen Degrees of Pianissimo". I tried out every kind of music on him, from seductive oriental dance-rhythms to Hebridean love-lilts; and from popular songs and marches to the great works of Bach and Beethoven. But not once, either then or in my three years of subsequent association with him, did he give any sign that I could discover that he heard a single note of anything I played.

Whether his unbroken silence implied a compliment or an unshakable conviction that it was not worth listening to, let alone criticising, is a riddle I have never been able to solve. I fancy it conveyed nothing to him beyond the fact that, as all animals use their feet and paws in some way or other peculiar to themselves, this was just my noisy way of using mine. Perhaps it was as well. Progress seldom goes hand-in-hand with Pride; and Conceit, which is Pride's Poor Relation, is never seen in her company: so no doubt the perpetual reminder of my unworthiness was very salutary.

And yet—amazing as it seems to me even now—it was as a *music-critic* that the Mongoose first voluntarily introduced himself to his benefactresses, and in a manner that was as dramatic and impressive as it was unexpected.

It happened like this. I was practising assiduously one afternoon when the Doctor, who had just dropped in for a cup of tea, asked if I would accompany her in a favourite song. We started off gaily and then became aware of some kind of disturbance. Strange sounds like Gr-r-r-r-r-, Pfit! ---- gr-r-r- pfit! Pfit!-Pfit!-Pfit!-*PFIT*! seemed to be mingling with the plaintive beauty of "Unmindful of the Roses." Looking up we saw the Mongoose, standing on his short legs and with the most ferocious expression on his little face, growling and spitting through the bars of his cage in the direction of the singer. It was so incredibly ridiculous that we both burst into loud laughter, whereupon the outraged animal gave us a perfectly annihilating look, and after a last explosive curse, turned tail and disappeared into his sleeve.

It was one of the funniest sights we had ever seen. But it was also *very* heartening. For not only had it proved beyond all doubt that the poor down-trodden creature had regained his confidence in himself and his opinions; but he had stood there just long enough to gladden our eyes with unmistakable evidence that he had completely recovered his health. He looked positively ablaze with vitality as well as anger. His eyes shone and his coat glistened; and the change from the dirty, draggle-tailed, cringing bundle of wretchedness of only ten days ago to the brilliant little person who had now so eloquently expressed his views to us was past belief. As for courage, one could imagine him saying "Oboe to a Goossens!" if given the opportunity, or even of spitting contemptuously at the Philharmonic Choir in a performance of the Choral Symphony conducted by Furtwängler in the "Kensington Gas-works" as the students irreverently called the Albert Hall.

After this public-spirited display, as one would expect, things began to move rapidly. The Mongoose is nothing if not alert and observant, and I can hazard a guess that during those few dramatic moments which I have just described, he had taken a quick glance round the studio and registered the impression that it contained things that might be worth looking into later on. The volley of curses that he had always aimed at my hand whenever it invaded his cage to bring him food, was replaced by a gentle growling that suggested a sense of self-importance rather than fear. Once I turned my head quickly and just caught sight of him standing erect behind his bars looking at me down his nose with a most supercilious expression, and—though he disappeared as if by magic when I ventured a remark—this was a very great advance.

Then one night when I approached his cage to cover it with his dark blanket, I noticed to my infinite satisfaction that he had forgotten to growl at me; and as I gently expressed a wish that he would sleep well I saw a slight but unmistakable movement towards me of the bulge in the grey sleeping-bag. I fancied there was something a little friendly and confiding in this gesture and felt sure that he was beginning to lose his fear of me.

Perhaps after all he was finding the cold strange land to which a cruel fate had brought him not *quite* so hostile and so terrifying as it had at first appeared to him. Alas! poor tiny wanderer! he was indeed "Far from the shades of Arabia!" But, although he was as yet quite unaware of it, his feet were standing on enchanted ground, and he was already within sight of a fabulous "Arabian Nights' Entertainment" which was soon to unfold to him, week by week and month by month, in all its mystery and glamour, until it filled his little life with such perpetual delight that it flowed over into our own.

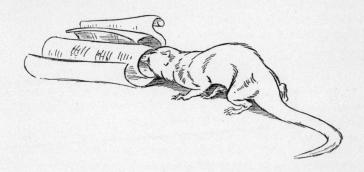

CHAPTER TWO

THE RECONCILIATION

After the Mongoose had made his debut as a music Critic with such dramatic effect one naturally felt that he deserved a larger field for his talents, and that the sooner he was encouraged to leave the shelter of his woollen sleeve and become acquainted with the world around him the better.

Before deciding on any course of action, however, there was much to think over; chiefly how, having once allowed him to escape from his cage, he could be persuaded to return to it.

It stood (sacrilegiously enough), as I have said, permanently on the grand piano, where it was safe from the attentions of over-inquisitive visitors, and was unlikely to be knocked, or even shaken except by the musical vibrations to which he seemed so indifferent. Once the Mongoose was on the floor the cage would be no longer visible to him; and, even if placed temporarily where he could hardly fail to see it, I thought it extremely doubtful whether anything short of starvation would induce him to re-enter it. To him it was still a prison and had been, until very recently, a place of torment.

The sleeve, however, had been and remained a refuge; and here surely was the solution of the problem, for were there not originally two sleeves in that old knitted frock of mine? It was easy enough to turn the remaining one into a long bag by sewing up the shoulder, and threading a strong woollen cord through the cuff by means of which, if the Mongoose did consent to enter it, he could be made a prisoner. If the cord were long enough, its two ends could be secured and manipulated from a distance. The next step was to close in the grate completely by a strong wire guard so perfectly fitted and firmly fixed as to provide complete protection from the fire. This took time; but at last all was ready and the cage-door was left open for an hour or so every day.

To my great surprise, a week must have passed before there was any evidence that the little captive had ventured through the door his jailer had left ajar: but late one afternoon I found the prison empty and knew that he had taken the plunge at last. I placed a saucer of bread-and-milk in front of the tall cupboard under which I felt sure he had taken refuge. I found it empty a few minutes later on my return from the kitchen; but the cage, well-baited with tempting food, on the floor close by, had no attractions for him, and any further experiments had to be left until the morning.

The next day a state of siege threatened to develop and so, anxious that he should not be starved into surrender, I decided to try the strategy of the second sleeve. Long hours of patience, with many sallies and set-backs, followed; and then, quite suddenly he ran straight into the decoy; and, as I was fortunate enough to pull the cords at the right moment, I had him safely, though ignominiously, "in the bag." I expected a great commotion of course, but a Mongoose is nothing if not surprising, and he just turned round, curled up and went to sleep, whereupon I tipped him gently into his cage, closed the door and left him alone to recover from the shock and return to his old routine.

The plan had worked better than I had dared to hope; and he accepted this form of transport from floor to cage after his daily excursions into freedom without any further trouble. Gradually he gained confidence to explore the studio in his own time and way;

and when tired or hungry was glad to avail himself of the comfortable closed conveyance which returned him incognito to the safety of his cage.

This was a tremendous step forward; and the next, which was to get him accustomed to my presence during his expeditions, followed very quickly. My pleasure can be imagined when I first caught a glimpse of him standing erect behind one of the legs of the piano, peeping round at me with a most inquisitive expression on his little face. Having survived this first act of audacity, he grew bolder and, mounting an armchair, stood on his hind legs, first on the seat, then on an arm and finally gracefully balanced on its well-upholstered back to obtain a better view of me.

After this, except that he never stood on his head or descended to the behaviour of rats and mice by running up the curtains, he scrutinised me from every possible angle while I sat enthroned on a hassock in the centre of the room to give full scope to his remarkable powers of observation. Eventually, having learnt all he could about me from a safe distance, he proceeded to take a detailed inventory of the contents of the room; and this kept him busy for a week, for a Mongoose is nothing if not thorough.

So far all had gone according to plan: yet we seemed to have reached a deadlock, for all attempts to establish any personal contact with him failed completely. He was determined to starve rather than take food from my hand, or even to drink from a long-handled spoon which I held out to him at arm's length.

Something had to be done: and, remembering what the Doctor had told me about the Mongoose always "taking the first step" in his introduction to human society, I decided to try an experiment. "Little Mongoose," I said, "you and I have *got* to be friends." And so one sleepy Sunday afternoon I locked the door, dragged the hearthrug into the middle of the room and lay down, fully-dressed, flat on my back with my arms wide, the palms of my hands uppermost and my eyes half closed. Then for hours I froze into immobility—and waited. Occasionally I caught a glimpse, in a tilted mirror on the wall, of the Mongoose as, like a lone, intrepid Commando who had planned a raid into the enemy's camp, he first slunk and then ran round and round in ever-narrowing circles until he had all but reached me. Time after time he streaked back into the shadows at a slight movement like the twitching of an eyelid, and the encircling dance began all over again. Eventually he explored me from the soles of my feet to the crown of my head, poking his nose into my tightly-closed eyes, running it through my hair, breathing into my nostrils and blowing into my ears. At last, though I have no record of what he thought of me, he appeared to be satisfied that I was worth his patronage; and so I rose, stiff and weary, to prepare the evening meal. We had both endured a very great ordeal and were very hungry.

And here I feel I should explain that this, on my part at least, had been an act of patience rather than of courage. I am not, alas, in the least heroic in the presence of savage beasts, and am quite incapable of "breathing gently down the nostrils" of a wild bull or a hungry wolf as recommended in an interesting book called *Talking to Animals*, by Barbara Woodhouse. I fear I should much prefer to breathe thankfully down the inside of a door that separated me effectually from such fierce creatures. In the case of the Mongoose I was quite convinced that he would not harm me in any way so long as I refrained from seizing him: and I felt pretty sure that, provided my patience proved stronger than my weariness, his curiosity would prove stronger than his fear. And so I had used the right technique; for I should never have tamed him unless I had allowed *him* to believe that *he* had tamed me which I am quite sure he did as long as he remembered me at all.

That night he ate from my hand. He even allowed me to stroke him from his nose to the tip of his tail: and when I beat up some raw egg, of which he was very fond, he drank it from a spoon, wiped his mouth, first one side and then the other, on my ankles, and signed a Pact of Non-Aggression by two yellow streaks on my stockings. When I said good-night to him, a little nose peeped out of his woollen sleeping-bag as a gesture of confidence and good-will.

Oh! that little nose! From the mustard-pot and a packet of pepper to the saucepan in which eggs were being boiled; and from the hot cinders in an ashpan to my workbox from which it emerged stuck with pins and needles, it was into *everything!* I kept a box of boracic ointment permanently on the mantelpiece, and he used to come to me and lift up his little face to have it anointed.

It was all well worth while, I am sure he thought, for had he not discovered, in that workbox of mine, a treasure worth all the Crown Jewels put together? A silver thimble that stuck on his little nose and could be blown off when it interfered with his breathing, run after and stuck on again! Life was really exciting

after all; and when once he had learned its hard lessons by bitter experience and come to realize that certain things, like fire and hot water, were hostile and vindictive when interfered with, but harmless and even friendly when left alone, he began to enjoy himself immensely and to regard my studio-bedroom as a well-equipped laboratory with endless possibilities for research and development.

There was one liberty, however, with regard to his person that he never permitted me to take, either then or at any further time. I must *never* lift him up without first covering his eyes. More will be said later of this obsession of his and its psychological implications: but I was made to realize at the outset that it was an unwritten yet inviolable law. To break it would be to lose his confidence for ever.

The sleeve that served as sleeping-bag in his cage was never discarded and remained for a very long time a source of comfort and security to him. The fellow to it, however, which had done such valiant service as a vehicle of transport had become rather unmanageable after months of hard usage, and I had to look round for something more practical to take its place.

Then Destiny, in a golden moment, took a hand in his affairs, and whispered in my ear the magic word "*boot-box*". I took the hint at once, and after procuring a good strong specimen of this serviceable commodity, I made a hole at either end, just big enough to allow him to go in and out easily. O! happy happy thought! A veritable treasure cave it proved to be in which a little Mongoose was soon to find, not only a cure for every ill, but joys unlimited, and in the end success and fame. He was delighted with it; and it was so easy to place my hand over the nose-end until he was in the right position to slip into his cage, that the problem of transport, as well as many other problems as we shall see, was solved once and for all.

At this point, to enable the story to proceed without too many digressions, perhaps a few details of the Mongoose's habits and characteristics might be useful. With regard to cleanliness, to house-train him presented difficulties. One cannot punish a wild beast straight from the jungle or desert, or even speak angrily to him without at once appearing as an enemy. The problem however in this case was nothing like so difficult as I had anticipated, for he was, without exception, the most inoffensive animal I have ever known. He had no strong odour, and, except on one solitary occasion, he never embarrassed me in any way by dirty habits. Some attempt to train him however was made; and, as sand or earth on a tray suggested something to burrow in and was scattered gleefully in all directions, I tried a shallow meat-tin which was easily washed out and could be kept in a dark corner. This, on the whole, was successful. He was scrupulously clean in himself and, although he never took a bath and never washed except for an occasional lick on the flanks, he was never verminous.

Of sex he seemed to be unconscious. He was an intellectual, and his creative powers were "sublimated"—i.e. absorbed into the work of research and love of high adventure on which his hopes were set.

Of his senses, unless I am greatly mistaken, sight and touch were pre-eminent. Furthermore, his organ of touch seemed to be his nose rather than his paws. How far scent helped him in his investigations I cannot say, but I never once saw or heard him sniff. He examined everything by touching it with his nose and gave the impression that it was by the feel rather than the smell that he discovered its nature. He used his paws in the manner of a burrowing animal to bring objects into the correct position for investigation. He was never destructive, except in the one respect that he could never see a hole in anything that was too small for him to get into without working feverishly with his paws to enlarge it to the required size. This however was a useful discipline for me, as it compelled me to keep my household and personal effects in good repair.

The occasion on which he embarrassed me was a professional visit from a very pompous musical celebrity who, as I could not offer him the amenities of a cloak-room, placed his very elegant broad-brimmed hat of delicate dove-grey felt on a cushion in the Studio. I had temporarily forgotten the Mongoose watching from a dark corner, and towards the end of a long conversation with my visitor I was horrified to see this hat careering round the floor and bobbing up and down like a thing bewitched. My visitor at that very moment rose to take his leave: the little culprit dashed to safety, and I was still more horrified to find the hat, with a little shining stream running round the rim, so limp and damp that it had to be sponged and dried before it could be restored to him, and then it was quite unwearable. In spite of my obvious embarrassment, profuse apologies and suggestions of a visit to Henry Heath at my expense, I don't think the great man ever forgave me!

As for the Mongoose, he seemed well pleased with his afternoon. "After all," his little face said quite plainly, though hardly apologetically, "it was a *very* funny hat." And when I remembered what it looked like when its owner took it away, I was inclined to agree with him.

CHAPTER THREE

HE DISCOVERS WORK
AND IS GIVEN A NAME

The next step, I should imagine, in the treatment of a Paranoiac, or person suffering from persecution-mania, after a measure of self-confidence had been restored to him, would be to provide him with some light, congenial employment that might lead to a corresponding degree of self-respect. I thought of many occupations that might hasten the psychological recovery of my little patient; but I could have spared myself the trouble, for he discovered work for himself, and later the intense happiness that can be found in it.

At that time I was faced by what was to me a particularly urgent and distressing problem. There was no cat in residence in the Doctor's house and, as I detested traps, my little kitchen had become infested with mice. They ransacked the larder, sorted salvage in the waste-paper basket, played on the pastry board, and sat in families, like the Bugginses, on the gas-cooker, waiting for their supper.

Dearly as I love all animals, I dislike the presence of these delightful but dirty little creatures in my food-cupboards, and I knew that the problem of their mass-extermination had to be faced. I found myself wondering how the Mongoose would react to them, and, by way of experiment, I took him in his bootbox into the kitchen one evening at the height of what appeared to be the mice's mass-celebration of some anniversary, and set him down on the table. What followed had to be seen to be believed for it defies description. There was a low growl, the bootbox shot on to the floor and out rushed a large, fierce predatory beast that I thought at first I had never seen before—a mighty hunter, with all his fur erect, his long tail bushy and magnificent, and his eyes like burning coals.

Now when a Mongoose is in a hurry one never sees anything of him except his tail, and one is lucky to see that. In the next split second I caught a fantastic glimpse of little tails disappearing in all directions before the onrush of a big tail which pursued and passed them. I caught the sound of a faint squeak that was never even finished; and when the dust and clatter had subsided I beheld the Mongoose, now reduced to his original sleek size, backing towards me in short sharp jerks, dragging the headless body of a mouse. I handed him his bootbox in silence and he pushed the corpse into it and came out again.

Then followed an astonishing performance. After what looked like some kind of ritual dance, he applied his nose to the end of the box, which now automatically became a combined hearse and coffin, and pushed it solemnly round the kitchen; after which impressive funeral procession, he dragged out the corpse, danced round it and devoured it with great enjoyment. Whether the mourning mice in the wainscote were silent and horrified spectators of this barbaric ceremony I have no idea, but no squeak, tail or whisker of them ever troubled my premises again. I had seen, and I must say, had been privileged to see what I had read of in books, the Mongoose as a killer—Rikki-Tikki-Tavi the ferocious, implacable, magnificent and victorious! But I never saw him in this rôle again, and the longer I lived with his shy and gentle ways and sensitive, kindly nature, the more impossible it became for me to associate it with him.

But what had happened that memorable evening was for him no mere adventure! It was no solitary classic historic achievement.

It was the beginning of a career that was to bring fame and delight to himself, and to us years of happy laughter. He had certainly proved himself an expert and merciful hunter, for death never came to any creature more swiftly than it did to that little mouse; but the unfortunate victim had quite unwittingly introduced him to a profession for which he knew without any hesitation that he had been born. He had discovered *work;* and from that moment the fascination of moving boxes from one place to another was to become a mania, an obsession that lasted for many months, and never in my knowledge of him lost its irresistible appeal.

This development seemed as curious as it was unexpected until (mongoose-like) I began to puzzle out some kind of explanation for it. I have already mentioned that the event which always gave him greater delight than any other was the discovery of a *hole:* and of course a hole to him was something that suggested a *burrow*. It was a potential hiding-place where he could "see and not be seen" and that was his idea of bliss. Now an Irishman described a net as "a lot of holes tied together with string" which is a very good definition of it indeed. He was also credited with mending his socks in his wife's absence by "cutting the holes out," which was not so good, though no doubt he realised that the holes were the only parts that kept clean, and if the socks were all holes they would never want washing. I applied this subtle chain of reasoning to the behaviour of the Mongoose. After all, what *is* a box but a hole surrounded by cardboard? And not only surrounded but controlled by it so that, unless you deliberately *put* rubbish into it, it never got out of shape or silted up like a hole in the ground! And then it was *portable* and could be moved wherever you wanted to take it and whenever you chose. *A portable burrow!* Just think of it! What *more* could a little Mongoose desire?

Of course I am not suggesting that he reasoned it all out as I have done: but I think it is quite probable that there was some connection in his subconscious mind between a box and a burrow; and after all why reason things out when you could see them in a flash as little mongooses saw so many things? Perhaps this also accounted for his delight in his silver thimble which had held pride of place in his heart from the moment he first beheld it. Was not this also a tiny potential burrow—a little hole surrounded by something hard, and bright and durable? He had tried in vain to enlarge it, to make it *big enough to get into* and, though he had temporarily given up struggling for the mastery of it, some day no doubt he would return to it, and fight it out all over again. And so it was also a silver portable conundrum, and he dearly loved conundrums even if they weren't silver! Then of course he may have liked the look of it and, if it hadn't interfered in its officious way with his breathing, he might have worn it on his little nose all day! Perhaps he was proud of it, too, who knows?— a kind of "Silver Tassie." At any rate it was a great treasure. The little fellow and I seemed to have the same kind of enquiring mind, and we were beginning to understand each other.

Whatever the psychological explanation of it may have been, the result of his discovery of a portable box was phenomenal. He thought of nothing else. Boxes of every conceivable size and shape (within reason, for he never misjudged his own strength or allowed himself to get over-tired), letters, packets, parcels, and (most coveted of all) rolls of paper or music were commandeered and moved at speed across the studio floor in all directions. Of course I collected most of them for him; but he added to the pile whenever there was opportunity, and the traffic soon began to be very heavy. And so, one day, as he stood proudly on his little hind legs on a biscuit-box to admire his fleet of vans, the Doctor and I solemnly christened him CARTER PATERSON, a name that stuck to him ever after, although he lived to deserve one of far greater dignity and beauty.

I must pause here for a moment to explain his method of pro-pulsion in these Herculean labours, for the name we had just bestowed upon him was a little misleading. He had certainly become a *remover*, but he was never in any sense of the word a *carrier*. I never once remember seeing him carry anything either in his paws or in his mouth. He either pushed with his nose, or dragged with his paws (used together with a rapid burrow-ing movement), in every transport operation he ever undertook. He often began by dragging an object backwards in this way in short jerks (as in the case of the dead mouse) until he had manoeuvred it into the correct position to be pushed forward by his nose in a clear drive. And by that I do not mean that he pushed and let go. He followed it up, with the weight of his body behind it, until he had driven it to its destination. Sometimes an awkward parcel would get caught up on the piano-pedals or other obstacles (for one must remember there was no policeman on point duty), and then he would work feverishly with his paws to drag it back into line before rushing it in scheduled time to the appointed place. What displayed his talents to the best advantage was a tightly-wrapped roll of music or paper. He could fix his nose firmly into one end of this, and then precipitate it across the room with such speed that the force of its impact on the opposite wall would surely have broken or at least dislocated the neck of any small animal except a mongoose!

All this sounds very rough and boisterous, but it was not so. He was too intelligent to be rough, and so light-footed and (after a little practice) so dexterous that he never gave the impression of creating a great disturbance. He could be *gentle at great speed*, which I consider a remarkable achievement. Then of course he slept, or at least rested a great deal during the day. He never broke anything except a balloon, though boxes made of fragile material got a little battered or lost their lids.

Unfortunately in his capacity of remover he had no idea of order or priority in his work. It was I, detesting slovenliness, who turned an old oak chest into a depôt or sorting-house for him. He would stand and watch me while I stacked his packages in this when it was time to cease work: and curiously enough he never seemed to remember that they were there, and never attempted to find them for himself, though as soon as the chest was opened he jumped in with an ecstasy of joy to push or toss them all out. This often raised a doubt in my mind as to whether memory was a very well-developed faculty in his mental equipment. It seldom goes with a very restless, creative mind in human beings, but I must not weary the reader with too many deductions. All my comments of course are based on my own reasoning and may not always be correct. It is only my observations that I can offer to naturalists with complete confidence, for I observed him with immense patience and meticulous care.

The only time I ever saw him use a paw in any sense of the word like a *hand* was when I was smoking. The ascent of the little clouds and whirls of smoke from my cigarette was a perpetual fascination to him. Having more than once applied his nose to the bright end of a cigarette and found it to be one of those hostile things that bit him, he kept his face away from it, but he would climb on to the table beside me, stand on his hind legs and try to push the smoke-puffs with his nose. Then up would come first one little paw then the other, (and always the right one first) in the prettiest way in a vain attempt to capture these little phantoms which so persistently evaded him; but the paw was never turned towards his face, and he knew nothing of forearm rotation. I think it probable, however, that had the smoke been in any degree tangible he would have been able to grasp and hold it. It remained one of the two major conundrums of his life and of his perpetual conscious search after knowledge. The other concerned the curious behaviour of a mat which will be described in the next chapter. He would look at me sometimes, as he wrestled with these perplexities, with the most absurd expression of utter puzzledom I have ever seen on any face, human or animal.

The recounting of two amusing accidents will bring this chapter to a dramatic conclusion. The first occurred when he stole an immense cream bun from the kitchen table. His feet skidded as usual on the polished linoleum; and when the bun broke up and covered his face completely with a dense mass of cream, he turned into a whirling, spitting catherine wheel of bun and fur. I added to his terrors considerably by washing his face. Then I put him to bed: but he was very upset in more ways than one and spent the night leaning out of his bunk and ringing for the steward. He was sick again the next day, but cured himself, as he always did if possible after an attack of indigestion, by drinking quantities of cold water with which he washed himself inside thoroughly, shooting it out afterwards in a fan-shaped pattern of watery streaks on the floor. Then, after a long sleep, curled up

B

in a warm place with his tail wrapped round him, he awoke in perfect health and high spirits.

The second far greater catastrophe was much enjoyed by the children who were the innocent cause of it. They had brought him, with the best intentions, a large rose-coloured balloon. Of course he was delighted and applied his nose to it at once when, to his obvious amazement, it sailed into the air and came down just where it liked. This was a new enchantment, and a new opportunity for conquest: and, after following it about for a minute or so he found that he could bounce it off the end of his nose, catch it there when it came down and bounce it off again. This was better still—and, incidentally, one of the prettiest sights it has ever been my privilege to see! All went well until a dark thought must have entered his little mind: "Why not jump on it? Then I could stand on the tittling top of the thing and find out what it's really made of!"

There was a bang—a rush—a streak—and a blur. When the children's laughter had subsided, I led them on tiptoe to peep at the shape of a curled-up, cowering, terrified little creature buried in the comforting folds of his old woollen sleeve, after he had been rescued from a perilous place under the hot grate. And so the firm of Carter Paterson was closed down "owing to circumstances over which he had no control." "Oh! He'll get over it," said the Doctor, as she slipped a sedative into his drinking water. "When once curiosity has taken possession of a little Mongoose he will get over anything." And sure enough he proved her right and was back at work within a week.

Now it often happens in the field of scientific research that one discovery leads to another. And so it proved in the case of our little friend, who was soon to experience the greatest thrill of his eventful life. After a week's rest of course his clever brain was more observant and alert than ever, and so, soon after he returned to the "office" he made another, and this time a breath-taking, epoch-making discovery. In fact it was not a discovery at all. It was a revelation—an Apocalypse.

And this is how it came about. In spite of that historic evening when he turned his beloved bootbox into a hearse and coffin at the obsequies of the defunct mouse, he never seemed to have been aware of it again as a self-propelled locomotive. To him it had been always a kind of private brougham, a closed vehicle in which he was transported without any effort of his own in comfort to his own home. I, of course, had preserved it and kept it out of his reach for this purpose. Suddenly one day—quite a dull one too, and one never knows what even a *dull* day can bring forth—he discovered it, lidless and bottom-upwards on the floor, through I suppose some carelessness of my own. He recognised it this time, because there was no dead mouse to take his attention, and he ran

in at one end and out at the other time after time. Then he pushed it from the inside and behold!—it *moved*! He came out again: turned a somersault, and pushed it harder again from the inside, and it moved still further. Suddenly a new light broke in upon him! Oh bliss incomparable, incredible, inexhaustible! Except for his tail (which was usually forgotten) he was covered as he always had been, but with this difference, *his feet were on the floor*. He could still see where he was going, but now he could *move*— anywhere, everywhere, among friends or foes, "seeing without being seen". Was ever any little beast so blest? Surely never before in the whole history of the Boot Trade had such an ecstasy of delight been bestowed upon any little living creature as was given to him that happy and never-to-be-forgotten day!

Quickly his clever brain sensed the possibilities of this new discovery. He began cautiously, moving slowly; then in little sprints and sallies until he got his bearings. Then suddenly the intoxication of the speed track took total possession of him. He flung caution to the winds: and before long, the Doctor and I stood helpless with laughter before the amazing spectacle of a bootbox with a little nose poking out of a hole at one end, and a long tail waving madly out of the other, careering round the room in one delirious stampede of uncontrollable ecstasy!

It was not the first time that he had made us rock with merriment, and it was certainly not the last. He was to give us nearly three years of laughter: and that was a great gift, made all the greater because folks with sordid lives and sad hearts sometimes came to share it with us.

CHAPTER FOUR

HE DISCOVERS FUN

AND BECOMES A COMEDIAN

Do animals possess a sense of humour? This is a question that I am often asked and I think the answer is: Yes, but much more rarely than is usually believed. The gambols of so many young creatures such as lambs, kittens and (most enchanting of all) fox-cubs, that so delight us are no doubt to a great extent just the overflow of high spirits. This, unless frustrated by fear, often develops into an elementary form of humour which we call fun and frequently mistake for it.

I remember a large, overfed and blue-ribboned white Persian cat dozing complacently on the top of some area steps near the Doctor's house; and, while I stood admiring her immaculate fur, a lean, ill-favoured, mangy-looking tabby sneaked up behind and gave her such a cuff over the ear that she was well out of sight before the lady had time to turn round, arch her back and spit in her direction. The expression of surprise on the face of the pampered Society Beauty was the funniest thing I have ever seen on the countenance of a cat. One could easily imagine Sally of the Slums laughing to herself in some sordid hiding-place; but there is no proof whatever that she did so, or that her triumph meant more to her than the settling of an old debt.

More convincing perhaps is the story, told to me at first hand, of a magpie who, as she watched a dog gnawing a meaty bone in the garden of the house to which they both belonged, conceived the brilliant plan of barking in the garage. The dog of course rushed in to drive off the intruder, while the bird disappeared and appropriated the prize.

I think, however, the authentic account, given by Colonel Williams in his book "Elephant Bill", of Burmese elephants filling the bells hung from their necks with soft mud to keep the clappers quiet while they steal out at night in search of love or adventure without rousing their attendants, is very hard to beat. But the elephant is a remarkable beast and certainly possesses, not only a sense of humour, but that sense of proportion which usually accompanies it, to a greater extent than any other animal.

Had Carter Paterson a sense of humour? I am inclined to think the answer is in the negative, and that, if I could have asked him quite seriously what he thought about the celebrity's hat and his game with it that brought me into such disgrace, he would have replied: "We were delighted, but we were not amused." Nevertheless I have no doubt whatever that, following his discovery of his portable burrow, he did develop a very strong appreciation of fun; and this, added to his abounding vitality, gave the (probably) false impression that he possessed a sense of humour. This love of fun, and his great natural gift of being able to look incredibly comical when standing on his hind legs to face an audience, are my justification for claiming for him the title of comedian.

By this time I had begun to find the continual traffic of boxes and parcels across my floor a little tiresome; and as he had proved capable of absorbing new ideas very rapidly, I racked my brains to find a new occupation for him. At first this was quite out of the question. He was obsessed with the excitement of running about with his box on his back and examining every long-familiar object through its window with new interest while nervous visitors to my studio mistook him for a poltergeist. Occasionally his box tilted up at the tail-end while he stood erect in it, with his paws dangling, looking very surprised and rather like a sentry who had gone to sleep on duty and wakened suddenly to find his rifle gone.

The next phase was to push boxes while remaining in his own box, like a train with the engine at the back; and this was so entertaining and provided him with so many new problems that the situation grew worse instead of better.

In due course the new enthusiasms cooled; and, with a view to encouraging him to confine his activities to one end of the room, I bought a large Indian mat, oval in shape and made of closely-woven grass or straw, as a play-mat or Magic Carpet to be kept permanently in one place exclusively for his own use.

The mat itself intrigued him enormously; and it was by experimenting with it that he discovered a new conundrum second only in importance to the mystery of the smoke-clouds from my cigarette.

This was how it came about. He was supervising my work one morning as I dusted my flat, when he found one end of his play-mat turned over and pinned down by the leg of a chair. Being very springy, this formed a tunnel which he realized at once had very great possibilities, and he began to run through it backwards and forwards in a frenzy of delight. When the chair was returned to its corner of course the tunnel disappeared and in its place was a riddle! *Where had it gone?* Quick as thought he dragged the mat-end over with his paws, and behold! the tunnel had come back: but as soon as he began to run inside it, like Macivity *it wasn't there!* He tried sitting on the flap and thought he had found the answer; but when he got *off* it in order to get *into* it, the thing had disappeared again so quickly that he couldn't even run after it or find out where it had gone! And that indeed was a new experience for a little Mongoose!

The fact that he never, even after two years of research, satisfactorily solved this problem by pushing something on to the edge of the flap firm enough to hold it down suggests that his intelligence was not of the highest order. This had already been evident in his continual failure to replace a lid that fell off a box in course of transit across the floor. The nearest he ever got to the solution of that difficulty was to sit inside the box and get the lid on his head. Perhaps it was just as well that his mental powers were limited; for his *persistence* in his search for knowledge about the nature of things that interested him was his greatest and most remarkable characteristic and gave the impression that had he been endowed with a high order of human intellect he might have conquered the world. He was at least *original*, and not derivative as so many pets become who spend their lives in the company of their owners: and that was something to be proud of, for Originality can often blow its trumpet in the face of Intellect without being ashamed.

As it was, the little fellow puzzled over his new problem until I feared for his sanity and tried to divert his attention from it by placing new and exciting objects on the mat for his consideration. When he pushed them off I pushed them back, and by so doing endeavoured to teach him that they belonged to his own private territory.

In the end he got the idea and developed such a stage-sense that he began to do comic turns there with his boxes and toys, even in front of a chance visitor who had the good sense to sit quietly at the far end of the room to watch him. This was interesting. Friends began to drop in to see the fun; and when we discovered that he had no objection to our laughing as much as ever we liked so long as we sat still, his play-mat became known as his "Little Coliseum," and he was launched on his career as a Music Hall artist.

At this point I would like to make it quite clear that Carter Pat (as he was called in theatrical circles) never played to a full house, except on one occasion when a party of children so terrified him that they nearly wrecked not only his career but his confidence in me. The room in any case was too small to constitute anything that could be called an auditorium; and, unless the stage was separated by a wide space from the spectators grouped near the fireplace at the opposite end of the room, he refused to play and went to bed in his bootbox.

To the Doctor and myself, a few friends or fellow-students and some sad and sick people who went away happier than they came, he played frequently and gave a great deal of pleasure; but that was all.

It is not possible here to give more than a brief description of one or two of his biggest hits. It must be remembered that no serious attempt had been made to train him. He improvised his

turns as he went along, so that when they were not new they were at least varied; and if he chose to run off the stage to try and find out what he looked like when he was on it there was nothing to prevent him from doing so.

For scenery I provided a large and very beautiful toy farmhouse in which lived a farmer and his wife, and this with a collection of farm animals, carts, etc., and a large Noah's Ark without a roof presented by a youthful admirer, occupied the centre of the stage.

He often opened his performance by rushing, with great speed and accuracy of direction, out of his bootbox in the middle of the room straight through the farmhouse door; after which his face usually appeared at one or more of the windows to be greeted with loud laughter. Perhaps he would follow this up by tossing the farmer's wife out of the front door into a box or (if he were lucky) into a farm-cart, and pushing her round the stage. Or, as I remember on one occasion, by helping a pathetic-looking rag doll out of the Ark and sitting with her in a box as if they were riding down to Bangor or off to Gretna Green; and then, just as the audience was beginning to feel romantic, he would throw her over and elope with Mrs. Noah.

The usually successful seating of his oddly-assorted passengers in the various vehicles at his disposal was accomplished with such rapidity that it was difficult to see how it was done. I think he usually tossed them in with his nose, and might even have treated the little light ones like counters in a game of Tiddliwinks, but I am quite sure he never carried them. If they missed the bus and flew over the farm-house he generally sent some more after them and then stood on tiptoe on the roof to see where they had gone.

The rapidity of his acting was astonishing and the expression on his face comical. In fact, it was just like Toytown gone mad and unbelievably funny with a real live animal as the central figure. And yet, so far as I remember, he never destroyed or even seriously damaged any of his toys. Underlying all the fun I suppose was that alertness, instinctive and unfailing, without which the mongoose could never have won his ascendancy over the mighty cobra. It was always there I fancy, though I am quite sure he was often temporarily unaware of it.

One unlucky day a lady in the audience presented him with a small perambulator containing two pink celluloid babies who were not even dressed. This was not in very good taste. Indeed it was a scandal for he was a bachelor and disliked children! My mind is a little hazy as to what actually happened that afternoon; but, according to a spectator, he flung the babies out and tried to persuade Mrs. Noah to take their place. When, as one might expect, that renowned lady flatly refused to be treated with such a complete lack of *comme il faut*, there was a heated argument during which the end of his tail became entangled in the perambulator-wheels. Then he turned and *spat at the audience!* There were no casualties, but the matinee ended in pandemonium.

It was the only time I remember when he disgraced his profession but the audience adored him for it. It was of course a very small world to which he played; but when, as occasionally happened when we least expected it, he took his curtain standing on his hind legs with his thimble on his nose, he was certainly that small world's darling!

Further descriptions, however, of this small artist's antics and absurdities might become tedious. The charm of his performance lay in its spontaneity; and I suppose it was, more than anything else, an exhibition of sheer high spirits which made his audience as merry as himself. This was no mere acting. It was pure, unadulterated fun. It was *Frolic* spelt with a very large Capital F and all the other letters running round it. If any sense of frustration still inhibited his once-tortured mind, he certainly left it behind when he entered the doors of his "little Coliseum".

As a mere amateur psychiatrist to little beasts and birds, I was beginning to be rather proud of my small patient. But there was still much that I had in mind to teach him. Fun, so essential to the young, and so healthy to mind and body at every stage of life, is not an end in itself; and, as many comedians know only too well, it is a poor substitute for true and lasting joy.

As time went on a certain *wistfulness* could be detected in the face and gestures of my little protégé, if not on the stage itself, in our quieter moments together. In his own little way, he was for ever reaching out after greater knowledge and those deeper experiences without which life's journey could hardly be said to have begun. We were still on the march: but another year was running out, and we had travelled further than we knew.

CHAPTER FIVE

HE DISCOVERS LOVE
AND COMES IN SIGHT OF FAITH

I have often noticed, when a forlorn and footsore traveller asks me to go a mile with him and I obey the command of Love and "go with him twain," that it is on the second mile that we find the view.

It was now two years since I first took it upon myself to act as guide and mentor to a little outcast brother in his journey out of fear into faith; and, on the whole, we had progressed steadily and without too many discouragements and disasters. Now we seemed to be breasting the hill after the long ascent and, looking down on gracious valleys and fair pastures, were already in sight of home.

39

Not that the journey had been by any means tedious. Far from it. How could it be in the company of so lively and entertaining a companion? But it had been exacting and often far from easy; for, although he was always faithful to me and followed no other, a false step or an angry word might have lost him to me for ever. As it was, he was the merriest of fellow-travellers; and we were kind to each other, but had never really been friends or known anything of fellowship in the real sense of the word.

The change came suddenly, as all changes did in my experience of this extraordinarily interesting little personality. That, however, is characteristic of the Mongoose. He may be shy in retirement where, being the most observant of all beasts, he lays his plans with care and skill, but in action he is swift and spectacular.

I was lying late in bed one morning, enjoying that blessed state of mind that lies in a mist of light between dream and reality, when I became aware of the Mongoose on the eiderdown moving stealthily towards my pillow. By great good fortune I had the presence of mind to remain motionless with my eyes half-closed, and so he came steadily on until, after standing erect for a moment to take a last look at my impassive face, he pushed his nose suddenly under the bed-clothes and, in a flash, had run in and curled himself up in my neck.

It was almost past belief, this act of confidence and affection, and for an interminable half-hour I froze in a cramped and uncomfortable position for fear of breaking the spell. When I could bear it no longer, I shifted slightly and began to speak to him very softly and slowly. To my relief, though he stirred uneasily once or twice, he made no attempt to hurry away; but later he slipped out and retired into a dark corner of the room to think things over.

The next morning he came again and, although he fled in terror when my hot-water bottle slid tactlessly to the floor, he returned to examine it. Then, after satisfying himself that it was harmless or at least well-intentioned, he rushed to me and finished his meditations under the bed-clothes.

By the end of a month this had become an established part of life's routine, the happy beginning of his little day; and before long he had not only grown accustomed to my movements, but submitted to my lifting him from one position to another under the bedclothes so long as he could not see what I was doing. I have already described in an earlier chapter this curious obsession of his—"fixation" would probably be the modern word for it. I could touch, stroke or even tickle him as much as I liked so long as he remained free to run away if he chose: but I must *never* take him up in my hands or into my arms—that is of course into my power—unless his eyes were covered. I think it placed too great a strain upon his trust in me to put both touch and sight (the great twin-sentinels of his citadel of self-preservation) to the test at the same time; and because one cannot reclaim any creature, human or animal, either from sin or from fear, without respect as well as love, I considered his wishes always in this matter, and in so doing I kept his confidence. To me there was something a little profound perhaps in its hidden interpretation, of which of course he was quite unconscious; for is not faith in its very essence "the evidence of things not seen"?

That he found this new and intimate fellowship with me very comforting and satisfying, both to mind and body, I have no doubt whatever. Week by week the confidence increased and the friendship deepened until he began to jump on to my knee and shoulder and, after unfastening the top-button of my cardigan with his nose, to run inside and curl himself up in my neck just out of sight. Often as I ate my meals, practised the piano, sewed or studied, I would be conscious of a fairy-like commotion, and then of a warm soft bundle under the collar of my woollen coat, quite motionless and perhaps asleep. In fact, I was soon in danger of forgetting that he was there and going out into the street where he might have taken fright and been lost for ever.

Let no one imagine, however, for one single moment that Carter Paterson the indefatigable had retired either from business or from his profession to become a member of the leisured class or one of the empty-headed idle rich. That was very far from being the case and would have been a shameful betrayal of his family tradition. He still commanded his fleet of pantechnicons; fulfilled his duties as expert collector and remover of goods; and, like a conscientious Customs Officer, examined, with meticulous care and attention to detail, every strange object, great or small, that was brought into the room. Luxurious he might be—and why not, indeed?—but never *lazy!* I think his acute mental activity and perceptiveness, and the insatiable curiosity and love of high adventure that he inherited from his proud, fierce but wise little ancestors, made it impossible for him to degenerate into a state of idle self-indulgence. Had he done so I fear I should have lost my respect for him and to a great extent, my interest in him also. As it was I was proud of the little creature's friendship; and I valued his love and trust very highly, for they had been dearly bought by careful study and unfailing patience.

Naturally the more exclusively he became attached to myself the less attractive he became to other people. I fancy however that, although he still noticed and examined the possessions and appendages of my friends and visitors, *he* had also lost interest in *them*. There had been a time when I could almost have believed that he compared the shape and size of their noses as he stood on tiptoe like a Court photographer studying them from every angle and in every position; but he had long ago arrived at the conclusion that all human beings were painfully slow and quite unintelligent with (perhaps) the exception of myself on whom so much depended.

Occasionally a visitor annoyed him intensely, probably by some vibration in the voice that affected his nerves. I remember a visit from a very distinguished old lady which took me completely by surprise because I had thought she was abroad. As we sat chatting together, I suddenly remembered that the Mongoose was down my neck, but decided to say nothing about it as I felt sure he would remain in hiding until she had gone. I was wrong. He must have thought she had outstayed her welcome, for he began to growl and rumble ominously in his secret lair. My visitor looked at me very curiously, thinking I might be ill, and she rose to take her leave. Suddenly from the neck of my cardigan just under my chin a fierce little face shot up and growled and spat at her so ferociously that she screamed and fell backwards over a chair. I had to rush the naughty little animal unceremoniously into the kitchen, lock him in and run back with all possible speed to restore, explain, and apologise, and finally to procure a taxi to take the old lady home. It was the second of only two occasions in my whole acquaintance with my little Mongoose when he embarrassed or distressed me by sins against the proprieties: and that, after all, shows a very high degree of virtue in a little wild beast from the Arabian desert.

There were occasions, of course, which I do not count, when, like every man of character and convictions, he felt bound to protest against outrageous behaviour on the part of other people. For instance, when the Guards paraded to Sunday morning service, at the church down the road, in their resplendent glory, with their band in full blare, he would streak across to the window, stand erect on the ledge and, with his nose against the pane, bombard them with such a volley of annihilating anathemas that it seemed a wonder they didn't surrender at once and give themselves up to a man. Fortunately the British Army was unaware of this assault upon its prestige or my little friend might have been conscripted as a regimental mascot.

Apart from a few dramatic incidents of this nature life went on very smoothly and happily for us both. I was attending at that time a series of lectures and classes of instruction in connection with my profession which necessitated my leaving him at home alone for five days a week instead of two; but, locked into the studio with his food and toys, he always seemed contented and able to amuse himself in my absence. Up to this time he had never shown any very marked pleasure at my return in the evening. But now things were changed, and I knew, as I turned my face towards home, that a little friend awaited me there and would be very pleased to see me. Not that there was any demonstration when I opened the door and called to him. The last little barrier of reserve that still remained between us restrained him no doubt from any display of excitement. What invariably happened was much more original and interesting than rough-and-tumble caresses. He stood erect, either on the hearth-rug facing me or by the side of my chair, with such an air of deference (in the old

English butler tradition) until I was seated that it was difficult to refrain from laughing. Of course I never did, for that would have been discourteous and also unwise to a degree. Then so rapidly that I hardly knew how he got there he was curled up in my neck; and that was all.

I felt the time had now come when he should be promoted from dining on a corner of the hearth-rug to occupying a place of honour at my little table, so I placed a dish, filled with a specially tasty portion of minced grilled steak etc., beside my own. Then, opening the collar of my woollen coat in which he was concealed, I invited him to take supper with me. He was not slow to understand and accept the invitation, and from that night onward (except on rare occasions when it was not possible) we invariably dined together. Sometimes, though he was unaware of it, I was *his* guest, for local shopkeepers often sent gifts of eggs, best beefsteak or lamb cutlets "with compliments—to the Mongoose", and it would have been impossible or extremely unwise to have allowed him to eat them all himself. I had been advised from the very start never to give him raw meat, which was too exciting, so his table-manners had never been deplorable. One might almost say now that they became exemplary if one could overlook that little habit he had of wiping his mouth—first one side and then the other—on my sleeve, which was not in the best possible taste. I got over that difficulty however quite easily by pinning the table-napkin with which I had provided him round my arm.

He sat, of course, on the table itself with his little dish in front of him, and on the whole behaved extremely well and ate very tidily. When he was satisfied and had rounded off his meal with a drink of milk from a spoon which I held for him, he stood on his hind legs and watched the funny way in which I disposed of *my* food. He never stared, but followed the ascent of fork or spoon from my plate to my mouth with great interest; and, though he occasionally lifted a little paw when he saw a particularly toothsome morsel about to disappear, as if to wave goodbye to it, he never snatched. No doubt he hoped for some small reward for his patience, and he stood there looking so fantastically human with his impeccable politeness of manner that if he had murmured

"You never can tell" with the inimitable intonation of Harcourt Williams I should hardly have been surprised.

He never appeared to be bored with me, and flattered me perpetually by his interest in everything that I did, except playing the piano. Like Robert Louis Stevenson he was "forever gaping at the Universe", yet with eyes wide and very wise in spite of all the riddles. And then of course I was a very big part of his Universe. One never noticed his silence. Words were not his medium of expression; and what did it matter when his face and manner expressed so much and so perfectly without them?

Looking back at him now across the long years I think his courtesy during these little suppers together is more remarkable than anything I can record of him; for one must remember that I had never actually trained him in any way whatsoever, and had never even rebuked him except in the gentlest of voices; also that less than three years before he was a little wild beast, a proud and savage hunter in a land where in all probability his people feared man as an enemy and had seldom (if ever) known him as a friend.

Sometimes the Doctor came in quietly during these little occasions of high privilege when we dined together, and sat, a deeply interested spectator, in a shadowy corner, but she never joined us at the table. Being the kind of physician that invariably puts a patient's interests before her own, she had always refrained from "obtruding herself", as she called it, upon the relationship between the Mongoose and myself. He, on his part, accepted her as one of the family but never transferred his allegiance to her. How much he benefited from her gentle influence and the atmosphere of unselfish love and compassion, as well as of happiness, with which she filled that house is beyond the power of any human psychologist to measure or comprehend. We do not know how far our influence extends. If we did, I think we should be afraid.

After supper came the lighting of my cigarette and the spectral ascent of the smoke-clouds of which he never tired. The lights were lowered, and the air became suddenly charged with mystery and excited anticipation. I leaned over the table and blew shapes and whirls, and little rings through big rings, while he stood erect, gazing at them as they floated up into the air and escaped in spite

of all his efforts to intercept them. This was his evening entertainment; his Indian rope-trick; the play to which the dinner had been the prelude; the detective story that was never explained and so remained a perpetual enchantment. I can see him now standing there with his rapt yet questioning look, his eyes shining in the glow of the firelight, and one little paw still lifted as though he were saying: "Isn't it all just wonderful!"

So the little wanderer had come home indeed: not to his native land, and not this time to an unknown refuge, but to a place of his own, that was safe and full of delight, and which he shared with his friend.

I too was satisfied, feeling that my work was done and that there was nothing more that he could learn from me.

But I was wrong, and there is another chapter to this book.

CHAPTER SIX

HE DISCOVERS WORSHIP
AND BECOMES A MYSTIC

More animals than you might expect are ready to adore man if they are given a reasonable opportunity: for man was made to be the priest, and even, in one sense, the Christ of the Animals: the Mediator through whom they apprehend so much of the Divine Splendour as their irrational nature allows.

C. S. Lewis, "*The Problem of Pain.*"
(Geoffrey Bles.)

On the old oak chest in my studio which, as I have previously mentioned, served as a repository for the boxes, parcels and playthings of my little protégé, had always stood a large and very artistically-attractive plaster figure of Saint Francis of Assisi of which I was very fond. He had just been preaching his famous sermon to the birds, and some of the more responsive little members of his congregation still brooded happily upon his arms and shoulder; while one, that might have been a sparrow, like a tiny St. John, nestled confidingly at his breast.

Little Carter Paterson had always been strangely attracted to this statue, and had shown a gradually increasing interest in it from the early days of our companionship; but he had always stood a little in awe of it, and would run round and round it on the oak chest, then jump down, peep at it from behind a friendly chair, and return for further investigations.

Now, after two-and-a-half years of familiarity with this mysterious figure, during which he had found courage to jump on to the arm and poke his little nose into the kindly face, I discovered him one day standing, erect and motionless, in front of it and gazing up with an expression of almost reverent wonder in his eyes as though he had suddenly recognised a friend. I cannot pretend to interpret his new impressions of it; neither do I suggest that there was anything supernatural about his attitude or the cause of it, but if St. Francis had been looking down upon him at that moment I am sure he would have smiled very tenderly. Thinking back now however upon the mental picture that it presents to me in the light of what happened later, I feel it was at least prophetic, or rather symbolic of a new phase of life and experience that he was about to enter.

For, little pilgrim as he seems to me now, he must already have come, in his progress, within sight of what might almost be likened to an unknown fane or temple, a place of peace where he was to discover what, on his own level, was akin to worship. And by what better name could such a place be known than the Little Sanctuary of St. Francis? And what more fitting statue, with welcoming arms outstretched, could be set up, within its sheltering walls, or even in its quiet precincts, than that of the gentlest of all Saints, the world's greatest human lover of all beasts and birds?

Apart from anything else, as a mere picture of the little wild creature in such an attitude, looking up into the face of his Patron Saint, it was one of the most enchanting sights that have ever delighted my eyes, and remains the undoubted masterpiece among the three incomparable and exquisite classic portraits of him that perpetually adorn the love-illumined gallery of my memory. Indeed, it was so appealing in its unaffected truth and beauty, and in its utter simplicity, and so unique as an animal study, that I persuaded, or rather bribed, a photographer to set up his big studio-camera at the far end of the room, and wait hour after hour for an opportunity to record it permanently with the aid of a primitive, but usually effective magnesium flash-lamp.

He, poor man, and his apparatus were submitted of course to as much scrutiny and investigation from every conceivable angle as if he had been an enemy agent to be secretly but remorselessly tracked down; and if he so much as changed his position, the Mongoose disappeared immediately in order to keep him under close observation from a concealed point of vantage. At long last, however, the photographer was rewarded by the sight of his little model self-posed to perfection before the image of the Saint; and, as the setting, with the dark smooth oak beneath him and the plain cream wall behind, was also perfect, our hopes of obtaining a superb portrait soared very high indeed. It was a chance in a million. The lamp functioned perfectly: the light flashed in all its brilliance, and the operator felt certain of his success. But, alas, when he took his head from under the dark cloth that covered his camera he found the Mongoose at his side, and almost on tiptoe, the very incarnation of astonished perplexity, demanding to know what in heaven's name the fellow imagined he was doing! The negative, when developed, showed a blur that marred a most beautiful photographic reproduction of the figure of the Saint.

The simple but profound truth, so superbly expressed by Dr. Lewis in the quotation that I have placed at the head of this chapter will, I trust, explain the implications of what I have recorded in it, and also, I dare to hope, afford some small measure of authoritative support to my comments, surmises and conclusions.

In the last chapter we reached the stage in the education of the Mongoose when love had all but vanquished not only fear but suspicion (which is fear in ambush), and had led him to repose happily in intimate personal contact with myself. He had travelled a long way from that nightmare circular track when my pitying eyes had first looked down upon his misery; and no one knows by what *via dolorosa* he had come to *that* unhappy place! He had served a strange apprenticeship since then, self-chosen in the workshop and on the busy thoroughfares that his imagination, or his instinctive imitation of reality, had built for him upon my studio-floor. He had gone on then from commercial success to the histrionic triumphs of his career as a comedian behind the footlights of his "Little Coliseum." His was already a history as eventful and adventurous in its own little way, as had ever been recorded of man or woman; and now he was approaching something that was stranger than anything he had so far known, but was mysterious and hushed and very happy.

It was not, however, his discovery of this little Shrine or Temple (if I may so metaphorically describe it) but my realisation of his discovery of it that was sudden and unexpected. Doubtless his own pilgrimage towards it had been long and unsuspecting, for no Muezzin from far-famed, fabulous Arabia had called to him from its shadowy watch-tower and no tinkling bells from the Minarets of his infant memory had guided thither his little steps. But it had been unerring, because it was Love that had brought him to this blest retreat where he could look with a new rapture into the face of the Being who now stood to him in the place of God.

For months before I had even suspected it, there had been a change in his attitude, not only to myself, but to everything that occupied the high places of his attention. Nothing had been lost that had been worth gaining: but all had been subdued and, at the same time, exalted—"sublimated" the psychologists would have called it. He still moved his boxes and parcels, but more as a pastime than as a profession. He still played with his toys, not so rapturously, but with a mature, and more delightfully delicate refinement of humour. I noticed this frequently, as for instance, when I watched him running Mrs. Noah in an empty soap-box round his play-mat for a gentle joy-ride, and then offering her the loan of his silver thimble from the end of his nose as he stood on his hind legs and looked for all the world as though he were anxiously enquiring if she cared to accept it. All this, of course, was quite unconscious humour; but it was fantastically, deliciously non-sensical, and it marked (or so it seemed to me) a great advance on the delirious excursions into the ridiculous with which he had so long delighted us. There was a touch of Barrie now in what he expressed, and more than a touch of Lewis Carroll in what he performed. I almost expected to see Alice and the White Rabbit appear suddenly and nod to me when I glanced again at Mrs. Noah in her green cardboard chariot and found that she had turned into a black-and-white cow from the Toy Farmyard; and it would have been quite easy to have imagined the ghost of a smile on the quizzical little face of Carter Paterson and to have suspected that he had his tongue in his cheek.

I thought at first all these quieter forms of his old activities might be the logical outcome of maturity. He was older and therefore less active and more comfort-loving. No doubt this was partly true; but he still worked for hours each day, and I was convinced that there was more in it than had at first appeared. What had happened, it seemed, was that by some strange process of psychological evolution, a transference of allegiance from *things* to a *person* had been brought about; and his mind was losing its hold on what was material and reaching up to something that transcended it.

It soon became obvious that I myself had become the pivot of his plans and the cause and centre of his preferences. I, so long the mere spectator of his triumphs, was now the one for whom they were paraded—the patron whose approval he solicited. Of course he could not reason all this out as I have done: but, after all, every truth to which the smallest fragment of reality belongs, has existed since the Beginning, and is neither created nor changed by all the human explorers, scientists and metaphysicians who reason endlessly, and write treatises and tomes about it. Also, as we know, great truths are often revealed quite suddenly to fools and little children.

The real climax that I am leading up to also came suddenly, and it was I this time who sat silent and astonished at what was not only the confirmation but the consummation of all my theories.

It began one bleak December evening as I sat reading over my studio fire. I was deeply engrossed in my book and, when I felt something strangely ethereal stealing noiselessly up my leg to the point of the knee, I must have jumped a little, for I caught sight of the Mongoose hurrying away into a dark corner. There was nothing new in his climbing up my leg, for he had long used it as a runway, and my knee as a springboard from which to jump to my shoulder and run to cover inside my cardigan. I knew instinctively that this was something *different*—a new approach—sensitive, and, in a delicate way, calculated. "This is interesting," I thought, and I called to him softly in a soothing voice: "It's all right, Little Carter Pat! Come and try again. Don't be afraid!" I put out my hand quietly and switched off the lamp at my elbow. Then I sat motionless with half-closed

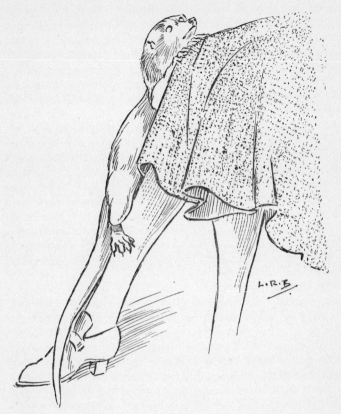

eyes, my book in my hand as though I were still reading—and
waited.

Presently he came, moving stealthily but steadily from the
shadows under the grand piano, until he had become visible in
the soft glow of the firelight. Then, so smoothly and with such
a delicate perfection of movement that it seemed unreal, he
ascended my right leg, stretched, and then flattened himself upon
it as a lizard will flatten itself on a stone under the warm rays of
the sun. Drawing my eyelids still further down upon my eyes,

and looking through the lashes, I saw him at rest, motionless but watchful, in a new and curiously dog-like attitude—his paws placed close together on my knee, his nose between them, and his eyes, in which a new light seemed to shine, gazing up steadily and adoringly into my face.

This was indeed something not only hitherto unknown to me but totally unexpected, and it could surely admit of only one explanation. It was the dawn of something very like a spiritual awakening. Unerringly my hand had led this little pilgrim ever onward and upward until he had out-distanced fear and, at his journey's end, had found himself at the feet of the Guide whom he was moved to worship.

After all, there is nothing *new* in this adoring attitude of beast to man. It began in Eden, where it was doubtless the frequent "outward and visible sign" of communion between them which was a type of and, on its lower level, analogous to the relationship that existed then between man and his God. The miracle to me is that, after so many thousands of years of estrangement, made hideous by cruelty and exploitation, "more animals than you might expect are ready to adore man if given a reasonable opportunity." This has been proved true beyond any doubt or controversy in these happier days when the Royal Society for the Prevention of Cruelty to Animals and other noble societies for the protection of the innocents have made the sight of happy fellowship between man and beast, in civilised countries at least, a commonplace.

I have seen adoration in the eyes of a horse before a worthy master. I have marvelled at it in the faces of the great cats that fawn and smile upon their keepers, in that of a great Indian hornbill as, with a grotesque beak like a pair of yellow garden-shears she fed her keeper with banana. I have seen it at very close quarters in the eyes of a London sparrow. And who is there among us that has not seen it in those of the dog, which perhaps alone among all animals is capable of self-sacrificing devotion, even unto death, and has the magnanimity to bestow its love unquestioningly on a cruel master who is utterly unworthy of it. I have always believed, and have proved it many times, that birds (especially the small varieties that are not predatory) are the most companionable of all creatures, but only a bird-lover is ever loved by a bird.

I was musing along these lines when I forgot the Mongoose at my knee, lifted my eyelids, and turned my eyes suddenly full upon him. And then another remarkable thing happened. He did not jump down and steal away into the shadows this time; but with his eyes still fixed on mine as though he were mesmerized, he slid slowly backwards, in a curious rhythmic zig-zag movement until he reached the floor. Then he was gone—and that was all. Probably the zig-zag movement was in some way connected with the ritual-dance of a mongoose before a snake; but why was it displayed to *me* at the very highest point, the apex one might say, of an act of worship? I sat puzzling over the mystery for some time and then rose and found my little friend under the eiderdown at the bottom of my bed, serene and apparently in a dreamless sleep.

Every night after this, during the last winter months before we parted, when we were alone or with the Doctor as sole companion, the same thing happened and it never varied. There was the silent, almost reverent approach, the ascent to my knee, the dog-like attitude, the steady gaze, for hours sometimes it seemed, into my face, the apparent adoration, and then the same withdrawal in its ritual, slow solemn, zig-zag dance when at last he met my eyes.

"You know," said the Doctor as we discussed this extraordinary behaviour on the part of my little friend, "after all, Carter Pat is still a little wild beast at heart. Instinctively he knows that he dare not look into the mesmeric eyes of his enemies, and that by speed and subtlety alone can he be sure of victory over them. Fear of the hunter's steady gaze is behind his retreat when you look into his eyes. That, I think, is the psychology of it; and perhaps (who knows?) unconsciously also it implies a reproach against man for his age-long betrayal of the trust reposed in him by God when he gave the beasts and birds not only for his use but into his care."

I sighed, for I was sure that she was right.

And now it is surely time that I brought this story to its close. The supreme gift of an artist is to know when to stop, and that may also be true of a teller of tales.

I must bestir myself therefore, and draw back the curtains in the little grey cottage that is now my home. For my garden of roses must be full of dew, and I can hear the blackbird piping in the poplars, and, far away, the skylark, in his radiant solitude, singing to the dawn-wind. It is five o'clock on a fair June morning, and I am alone with the unknown day.

It is as though I had just returned, a little weary in mind but refreshed in spirit, from an excursion into a far-distant land, once so familiar, then so long-forgotten. Memory, at the bidding of desire, had commissioned me to bring back from thence an authentic record of all that I could recapture of the history of a little long-lost friend, and this I have most faithfully endeavoured to do to the best of my ability.

It has been a strange experience, this journey into the past which, contrary to my expectations, became suddenly so much more real and vivid than the present, and was full, not of shadows, but of happy laughter with only here and there a trace of tears.

No doubt I have forgotten much that might have been of interest, especially to the scientific mind, but what I have set down was revealed to me with such clarity and conviction that it can hardly fail to give at least a fair and adequate impression of the personality it was intended to portray.

This, however, is not all that I had set out to do, and in attempting, through the medium of this little book, to present to its readers and critics a reasonably true psychological study of a little wild beast that I had almost (though not completely) tamed, I set myself a very difficult and exacting task. And when I say *reasonably true* I am thinking, not of the actual facts in the history of the Mongoose (the truth of which is not in question) but of my deductions from them and my interpretation of their significance, which must of necessity be largely hypothetical.

There is nothing easier for a Lover of Animals than to exaggerate the intelligence of a specially beloved and favoured one, and this pitfall I have also endeavoured to escape. If there is one thing of which I cannot be in any doubt with regard to Carter Paterson, it is that he came in the end to love me and to look upon me with some degree of adoration. Fragile that love may have been, and poised precariously between faith and fear (for if I had once lifted my hand to strike him it might have been irrecoverably lost), yet nevertheless it was there.

My little Mongoose, however, was no pampered pet. Indeed I doubt if his restless intelligence would have allowed him to be

degraded into one, and I certainly never allowed him the opportunity of putting it to the test. But he became a wonderful companion, and (except for my beloved sparrow of more recent years who became part of my soul and had no rival) he was, far and away, the most lovable and interesting creature I have ever known.

All this was long ago. I do not know to what age an Arabian Mongoose may live, but mine must have died long since. The beloved Doctor has gone too—she who first found the balm for his little sorrows as she strove to find it for those of every living thing that came in contact with her. Heaven, where no doubt she is a Companion of Honour, is the richer for her now; and who can say, and with any certainty, that he of the little loving heart and the little questing mind is not with her there?

So now my little tale is told, and for the last time the vision that compelled me to its telling fades. Its waning light falls softly on a little figure at my knee—a little wild thing happy and at rest—with shining eyes gazing up into my face. For there my little lover of conundrums had found at last the meaning of all things, and an unconscious realisation of the great truth that where Love is first all else falls into line.